Traditional
MAORI LEGENDS
Ngā Tai Kōrero

REED

Warren Pohatu

Dedication
To Manaia-o-te-Rangi and Erana-Jade

Published by Reed Children's Books, a division of Reed Publishing (NZ) Ltd,
39 Rawene Rd, Birkenhead, Auckland. Associated companies, branches and
representatives throughout the world.

Reed Publishing (NZ) Ltd
Te Karuhi tā tāpui o Reed (Aotearoa)

Established in 1907, Reed is New Zealand's largest
book publisher, with over 300 titles in print.

For details on all these books visit our website:
www.reed.co.nz

ISBN 1 86948 867 9

© 2000 Warren Pohatu

The author asserts his moral rights in the work.

First published 2000
Reprinted 2001, 2003

Printed in New Zealand

CONTENTS

MAUI AND THE FISH

Maui is one of the most famous characters in Maori folklore. This legend tells how Maui caught a huge fish which eventually became the North Island (Te-Ika-a-Maui) of New Zealand. The canoe or waka from which he caught the fish became the South Island (Te-Waka-a-Maui).

Maui was not a keen fisherman, and he also had the reputation of being a trickster. For these reasons his older brothers hated taking him with them when they went fishing. He was always playing practical jokes, and would often question the authority of his elders.

One day Maui's wife was nagging him to do something. She told him he was lazy, and said that he should help her with the chores. Maui became tired of her nagging and decided that he too would go out to fish the great oceans of Tangaroa.

Before leaving to go fishing, Maui went to the sacred burial cave of his ancestors. He took the jaw bone of his grandmother and fashioned a very special fish hook from it. Then he set out in his canoe.

When he arrived at the fishing grounds Maui's brothers refused to give him any bait, but this did not deter Maui. He made his nose bleed, and dripped blood onto his hook. Then he cast his line into the sea. Before long a fish took his bait. Maui struggled hard with the fish, and eventually he managed to haul it up. It was the biggest fish anyone had ever seen.

Today Maui's fish, Te-Ika-a-Maui, still remains on the surface of the sea. According to Ngati Porou tradition the first part of the fish to break the surface of the water was the summit of Mt Hikurangi. It was the first point to see the sun. And today Mt Hikurangi, on the east coast, is the first place to see the sun each and every morning.

PAIKEA AND THE WHALE

Paikea (who some people call Kahutiaterangi) is a very famous ancestor who lived on the east coast of New Zealand. He was a son of Uenuku Maraetai. Uenuku had a number of sons, including Ruatapu. Although Paikea and Ruatapu shared the same father, they had different mothers.

Paikea's mother was the principal wife of Uenuku, whereas Ruatapu's mother was a slave who had been captured in battle. One day when Uenuku made reference to this fact Ruatapu became enraged. He devised a plan to get rid of Paikea, hoping that he might then win favour with his father.

Ruatapu built a canoe which he called *Tutepewarangi*. When it was ready for its maiden voyage he asked that all the eldest sons of the chiefly families in the district be his crew. This included Paikea. Ruatapu planned to take his canoe to a point known as Te Huripeiata, and here capsize it and drown his unsuspecting crew.

On the day of the maiden voyage Ruapatu and his crew sailed out to Te Huripeiata, where Ruatapu immediately sabotaged the canoe. Then without warning he set upon his crew, managing to drown them all except Paikea, who had recited ancient chants to summon help from his ancestors.

In no time at all Paikea's prayers were answered, and a taniwha was sent in the form of a whale to spirit him away to safety. Paikea landed at Ahuahu (Mercury Island), then moved to the Whakatane area where he met Huturangi and her family. He married Huturangi and eventually they moved to Whangara, on the east coast of the North Island, where they settled.

Paikea's descendants remain at Whangara to this day. And on their meeting house is carved a figure of Paikea riding the whale.

KUPE AND THE GREAT OCTOPUS OF MUTURANGI

Kupe is another very important ancestor. It is he who is credited with discovering Aotearoa, several centuries before the main migration of our forefathers from their island homelands.

Kupe lived with his family in Hawaiiki. There they planted crops and fished the bountiful oceans. Often they would set long lines out past the reefs to harvest the abundant fish life that thrived in these waters.

At the same time there lived in Hawaiiki a tohunga named Muturangi who kept a giant octopus as a pet. One day Muturangi's mischievous octopus began to steal the bait from Kupe's lines. At first it was just a few hooks that were robbed, but over time the octopus became greedy and took all the bait. This meant that no fish were caught.

When Kupe learnt that the octopus's trickery was the reason for the declining catches, he decided he would capture this nuisance and kill it. The octopus fled from Hawaiiki to Aotearoa, and Kupe and some others gave chase in his waka *Matahourua*. They caught up with the octopus at Raukawa (Cook Strait), where they fought a great battle with the monster, hacking at its arms.

Finally Kupe killed the great octopus. He then cut out its eyes and placed them on some rocks. He named the place Nga Whatu, which means 'The Eyes' (its English name is The Brothers).

After his victory Kupe spent some time exploring this new land, before returning to Hawaiiki to tell the people there of his find. In time he would return.

8

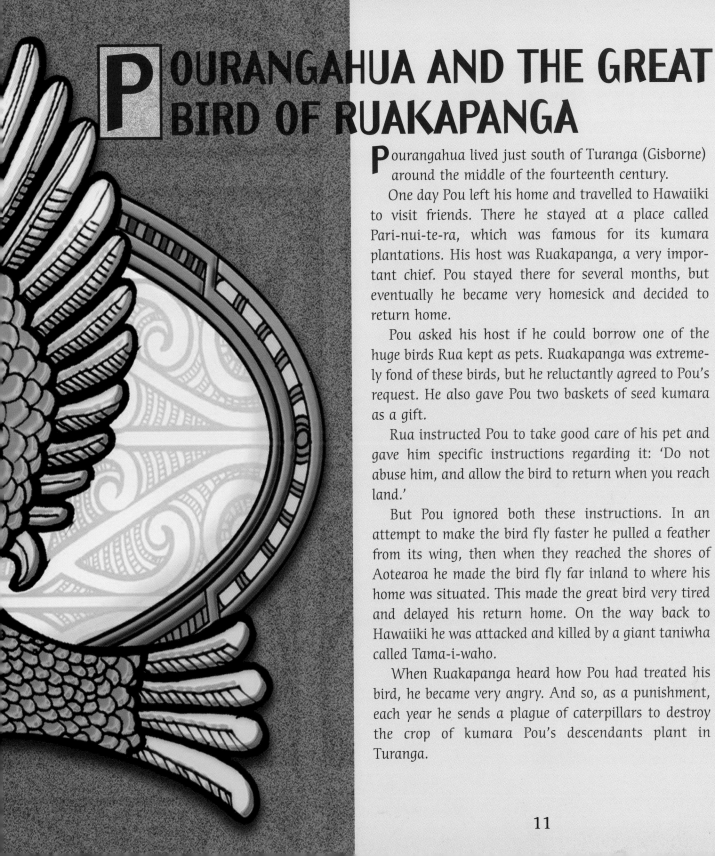

POURANGAHUA AND THE GREAT BIRD OF RUAKAPANGA

Pourangahua lived just south of Turanga (Gisborne) around the middle of the fourteenth century.

One day Pou left his home and travelled to Hawaiiki to visit friends. There he stayed at a place called Pari-nui-te-ra, which was famous for its kumara plantations. His host was Ruakapanga, a very important chief. Pou stayed there for several months, but eventually he became very homesick and decided to return home.

Pou asked his host if he could borrow one of the huge birds Rua kept as pets. Ruakapanga was extremely fond of these birds, but he reluctantly agreed to Pou's request. He also gave Pou two baskets of seed kumara as a gift.

Rua instructed Pou to take good care of his pet and gave him specific instructions regarding it: 'Do not abuse him, and allow the bird to return when you reach land.'

But Pou ignored both these instructions. In an attempt to make the bird fly faster he pulled a feather from its wing, then when they reached the shores of Aotearoa he made the bird fly far inland to where his home was situated. This made the great bird very tired and delayed his return home. On the way back to Hawaiiki he was attacked and killed by a giant taniwha called Tama-i-waho.

When Ruakapanga heard how Pou had treated his bird, he became very angry. And so, as a punishment, each year he sends a plague of caterpillars to destroy the crop of kumara Pou's descendants plant in Turanga.

TUTANEKAI AND HINEMOA

The tale of Tutanekai and Hinemoa is a classic Maori love story. These two lived in the Rotorua district several generations ago, not long after Te Arawa people settled in the area.

Tutanekai was the illegitimate son of Whakaue and lived with his father's people on Mokoia Island in Lake Rotorua. His real father was actually Tuwharetoa, who slept with Tutanekai's mother during Whakaue's absence. Hinemoa was the high-ranking daughter of Te Umu-karia, a highly respected and very powerful Te Arawa chief.

One day Hinemoa's people held a sporting competition at their pa, Owhata. Tutanekai attended with his father, Whakaue, and their finest athletes. As soon as they met, Tutanekai and Hinemoa felt attracted to each other and very soon, as young people often do, they fell in love. Soon they were inseparable. When it was time for Tutanekai and his people to return home to Mokoia, Tutanekai boldly asked for Hinemoa's hand in marriage. But her father, Te Umu-karia, refused. Tutanekai was illegitimate, and so did not meet Te Umu's high standards. Tutanekai and Hinemoa were devastated.

Tutanekai reluctantly returned with Whakaue to Mokoia. Every night he would play his flute to lament his loss, and the sad tune drifted across Lake Rotorua. Hinemoa could hear the music, and one night she could stand it no longer. She decided to swim to Mokoia Island.

Hinemoa set out from the shores of Lake Rotorua and eventually she reached the island, where she crept into a warm pool. When one of Tutanekai's slaves came to the pool to wash he was startled by the stranger. Hinemoa told him who she was and he rushed back to the village to inform his master. Tutanekai and Hinemoa were then joyously reunited.

RATA AND THE BIRDS OF THE FOREST

Rata lived many generations before our ancestors migrated to Aotearoa. He was a descendant of Maui and lived with his family in Hawaiiki.

One day Rata decided he would build himself a canoe. He found a suitable tree in the forest and set to work to fell it. He worked long and hard forming his canoe, but by late in the day he had not finished, so he decided to complete his task the next day. He returned home to sleep.

When he returned the next morning, to his utter amazement the tree was again upright and standing as if nothing had happened. Rata was very confused, but he again felled the tree and began work on his canoe. Once again he had not finished by the end of the day, so he decided to complete the canoe the following day.

When he returned the same thing had happened — the tree was again standing. Rata was now very angry, and demanded loudly, 'Who is it that plays this trick on me?' Then he again felled the tree. But this time, instead of returning to his home at the end of the day, Rata hid in the bushes nearby, waiting to catch the trickster.

Before long all the birds of the forest appeared. They began to gather up all the wood chips and replace them. They slowly put the tree back together.

Rata jumped out from his hiding place and confronted the army of birds. 'What's going on?' he demanded.

One of the birds told Rata that he had not asked Tane, the god of the forest, for permission to use the tree, and Tane had instructed them to resurrect it.

Rata now realised his error and prayed to Tane for forgiveness. Tane then instructed the birds to help Rata complete his task. Soon a beautiful canoe was built. Rata gave thanks to Tane for the gift of one of his children.

HINETITAMA: THE FIRST CHILD

It is said that it was Tane who created the first woman. He took red clay from the bosom of his beloved mother, Papatuanuku (mother earth), and lovingly moulded it into the form of a woman. He named this woman Hineahuone. Then Tane pressed his nose against hers and breathed life into her through his nostrils. Thus began a very special bond between men and women.

Tane married Hineahuone and soon she became pregnant by him. Hineahuone gave birth to a daughter who was named Hinetitama. Tane had many other children but Hinetitama was the first human child. Thus began the development of mortal man.

Hinetitama was raised by her mother and eventually grew up to be a very beautiful woman. Tane then married Hinetitama and soon they too had children.

For a time Hinetitama was unaware that Tane her husband was also her father. Then, one day Hineahuone told her daughter that Tane was indeed her father. So great was Hinetitama's shame that she ran away to the underworld. Tane pursued her but she would not return, preferring to stay in the darkness to hide the shame that had engulfed her. She vowed never to return to the world of light, and she changed her name to Hinenuitepo (woman of the darkness).

Tane continued to plead with her to return, but she refused, telling him to return to the world of light to care for their children there. When they died, she said, she would welcome them to the realm of night.

And to this day Hinenuitepo remains in the underworld to care for the many descendants who have followed her there.

NGAKE AND HINEWAIHUA

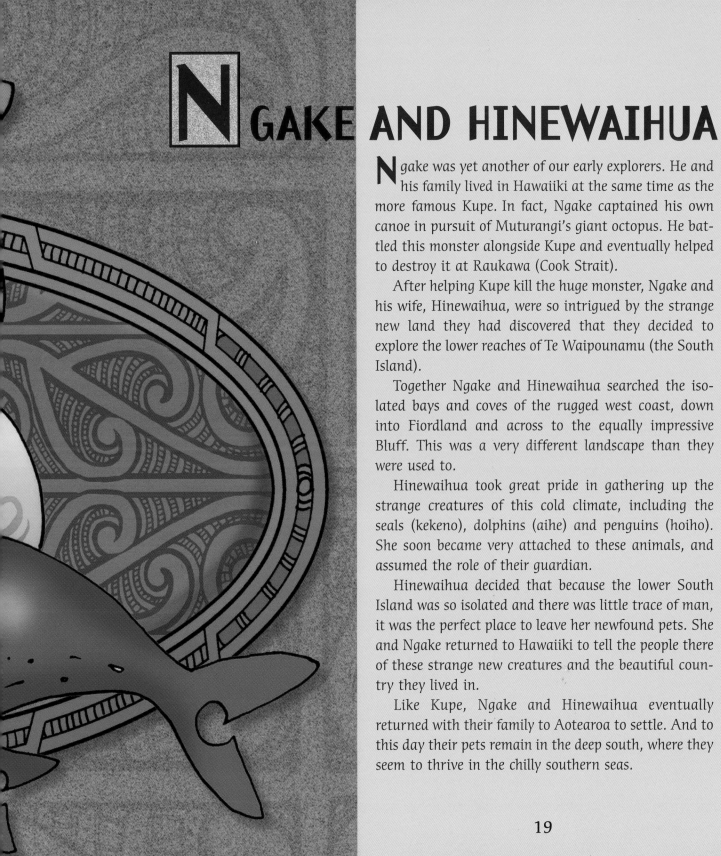

Ngake was yet another of our early explorers. He and his family lived in Hawaiiki at the same time as the more famous Kupe. In fact, Ngake captained his own canoe in pursuit of Muturangi's giant octopus. He battled this monster alongside Kupe and eventually helped to destroy it at Raukawa (Cook Strait).

After helping Kupe kill the huge monster, Ngake and his wife, Hinewaihua, were so intrigued by the strange new land they had discovered that they decided to explore the lower reaches of Te Waipounamu (the South Island).

Together Ngake and Hinewaihua searched the isolated bays and coves of the rugged west coast, down into Fiordland and across to the equally impressive Bluff. This was a very different landscape than they were used to.

Hinewaihua took great pride in gathering up the strange creatures of this cold climate, including the seals (kekeno), dolphins (aihe) and penguins (hoiho). She soon became very attached to these animals, and assumed the role of their guardian.

Hinewaihua decided that because the lower South Island was so isolated and there was little trace of man, it was the perfect place to leave her newfound pets. She and Ngake returned to Hawaiiki to tell the people there of these strange new creatures and the beautiful country they lived in.

Like Kupe, Ngake and Hinewaihua eventually returned with their family to Aotearoa to settle. And to this day their pets remain in the deep south, where they seem to thrive in the chilly southern seas.

NGATOROIRANGI

Ngatoroirangi was a very famous priest who travelled to Aotearoa onboard the canoe *Te Arawa*. He had an eventful journey, and almost sent the canoe to oblivion by summoning the giant taniwha Parata. He ordered the taniwha to swallow *Te Arawa* because he suspected his wife was sleeping with Tamatekapua, the captain of the waka. Fortunately, at the last minute Ngatoroirangi called for Parata to leave the canoe, and soon calm was restored to the oceans.

Eventually *Te Arawa* arrived safely on the shores of Aotearoa, and the members of her crew began to explore the new lands. Ngatoroirangi ventured inland, his journey soon taking him to the central North Island. There he discovered the mountains just beyond Taupo-nui-a-Tia.

Ngatoro decided he would climb to the summit of the mountain we now call Ngauruhoe, to claim the mana of this entire territory. His people warned him of the extreme cold he would encounter, but Ngatoroirangi and his slave set out to climb the mountain. As they drew closer to the summit the cold began to affect the slave, who grew very weak. Ngatoro continued upward, but the cold began to affect him as well. Then Ngatoro began a chant, summoning help from his sisters Te Pupu and Te Hoata, who were both still in Hawaiiki.

His sisters heard their brother's prayers drifting down from the clouds, and they immediately sent fire from the volcanoes at home. The fire rushed beneath the soil, exploding out as it reached the summit of Ngatoro's mountain. Ngatoro was warmed by the fire and was able to return to his people below, having claimed mana over these territories forever. But it was too late for his slave, who perished in the snow.

Even today, the smoke from Te Pupu and Te Hoata's fire can sometimes be seen coming from the top of the mountain.

TANE AND THE THREE KETE

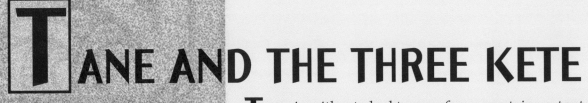

Tane is without doubt one of our most important gods. He is one of the many children of Ranginui (the sky father) and Papatuanuku (mother earth). In fact, it was Tane who separated his parents by lying on his back and pushing up with his feet. Tane allowed the sun to shine between his parents, bringing light and warmth to the world, and allowing plants to grow and thrive.

As we have seen, Tane was responsible for creating the first woman, Hineahuone, from the soil. Through Hinetitama, the daughter of Tane and Hineahuone, mortal man was born.

Having created man and provided him with food and a source of warmth from his great forests, Tane decided to gather together knowledge and understanding for people to enjoy and govern themselves by.

The knowledge Tane craved was held in the highest heavens of the sky. Tane decided to climb these heavens in search of this knowledge. As he searched, he collected sacred knowledge and stored it in his vast memory.

He finally reached the twelfth heaven, and there among the gems of our traditions he discovered three kete. These kete contained everything man required to fully appreciate his existence. Tane collected these kete and secured them to himself. He then began his treacherous descent to Papatuanuku.

When Tane finally reached the realm of humans he gifted these kete and all the wisdom within to them, and charged them with protecting this knowledge forever. It is this sacred knowledge that our ancestors have used to guide our people through the many generations into the strange new world of today.

TANGOTANGO AND TANE

Tangotango is one of our little-known ancestors who lived several generations before the migration of our people to Aotearoa. In Ngati Awa tradition he is remembered as a son of Rangi and Papa. He was the younger brother of Tane.

Tangotango is considered the father of the light. His children include Te Ra (the sun), Te Marama (the moon), Nga Whetu (the stars), Te Hinatore (phosphorescence), Te-Pari-Kiokio (glow-worms) and Hineraua-moa (moa-plume woman, representing faint light).

When Tane saw how brightly these lights shone, he was extremely envious. He asked that he be given a child to light the world with. Tangotango agreed and first gave his daughter Hinerauamoa, but her light was far too faint. Then he gave Te-Pari-Kiokio to Tane, but that light was not bright enough either. Tangotango then gave Te Hinatore, but still the light was not bright enough for Tane.

Soon Tane also had Nga Whetu and Te Marama to light up the night sky. The stars glistened in the heavens and the moon glowed like a giant fire-fly. Yet still Tane was not happy.

Tangotango became angry when he realised that his brother had tricked him out of his children, and he sent his eldest, Te Ra, to destroy Tane and his realm upon the earth. But Tane was able to avoid the red-hot rays of Te Ra. He thrust his father Rangi high into the heavens, then he tossed Te Ra up into the sky so that his rays could not harm Tane's realm upon the earth.

Te Ra's rage against his uncle soon subsided and he settled into the rhythm of providing light and warmth to Tane's kingdom. To this day Te Ra still brings the life-giving energy of his rays to share with the many children of Tane.

RONA AND THE MOON

Many, many generations ago Rona lived with her family in a small village nestled in a valley next to a flowing river.

One night, Rona had no sooner got comfortable and warm in her bed when her husband asked for a drink of water. Rona grumpily got up to fetch water from the taha (gourd) in the corner of her house. Alas, it was empty. When she told her husband, he insisted she go down to the river to collect water, for he was very thirsty. Rona snatched up the taha and stormed out the door.

Carrying her taha, she followed the trail down to the rock pools by the light of the full moon. She soon filled her taha and began the journey home, all the while muttering to herself.

Suddenly the moon disappeared behind a cloud. Rona stumbled and fell. She grazed her knee on the rocks and screamed in pain. Then Rona turned her head toward the moon and cursed it several times. The moon heard her and became very angry. He said to her, 'Rona, I am not to blame for your current plight.'

Rona again cursed the moon for disappearing and causing her to fall. This enraged the moon even more, and as punishment he decided to seize her and draw her up to him. Rona held fast to her taha, then as she felt herself being drawn toward the moon she clung to a nearby tree. But the pull of the moon was far too strong, and it ripped the tree's roots from the ground. Rona was carried up to the moon, still clutching the tree and her taha. To this day she remains in the moon, sitting next to the tree with her taha in her hand.

MAUI AND THE SUN

There are numerous tales of Maui and his adventures. He is a source of pride and inspiration as he constantly overcomes the odds and succeeds where others would succumb to failure. The story of Maui and the sun simply confirms his position as our greatest tutu (prankster).

In ancient times the sun travelled much faster across the sky than it does today. The days were very short indeed, with hardly enough time for people to hunt or fish. Nor could they tend to their gardens. Many people complained that no sooner had they got up, had breakfast and prepared their tools than the sun would begin its descent into night.

Maui decided that he would snare the sun, and make him travel much more slowly. That way everyone would have plenty of time to complete their tasks.

Maui's brothers scorned his plan, but he was not deterred and prepared a special net. Then he again asked his brothers to help, and they eventually agreed.

Maui and his brothers spread their net across the sky and anchored it to the ground. When the sun rose the next day he rushed straight into the net and became entangled in it. Maui recited a chant to pacify the sun, then he commanded him to travel slowly. At first the sun refused. Maui recited yet another chant, and eventually the sun was subdued.

Maui instructed the sun as to what was a more suitable pace, then released him. To this day the sun continues to travel at that same leisurely pace, thanks to Maui.

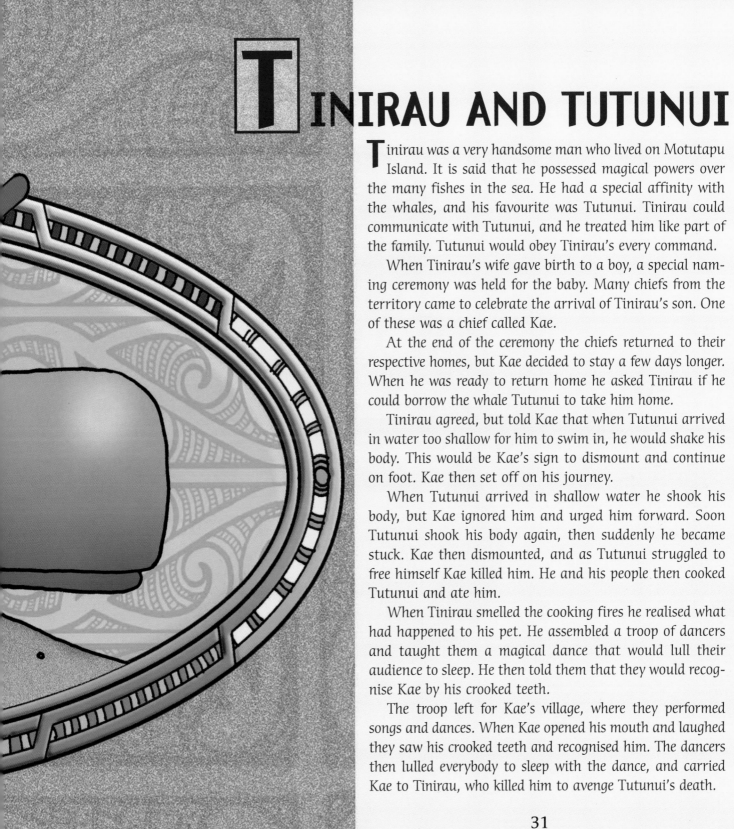

TINIRAU AND TUTUNUI

Tinirau was a very handsome man who lived on Motutapu Island. It is said that he possessed magical powers over the many fishes in the sea. He had a special affinity with the whales, and his favourite was Tutunui. Tinirau could communicate with Tutunui, and he treated him like part of the family. Tutunui would obey Tinirau's every command.

When Tinirau's wife gave birth to a boy, a special naming ceremony was held for the baby. Many chiefs from the territory came to celebrate the arrival of Tinirau's son. One of these was a chief called Kae.

At the end of the ceremony the chiefs returned to their respective homes, but Kae decided to stay a few days longer. When he was ready to return home he asked Tinirau if he could borrow the whale Tutunui to take him home.

Tinirau agreed, but told Kae that when Tutunui arrived in water too shallow for him to swim in, he would shake his body. This would be Kae's sign to dismount and continue on foot. Kae then set off on his journey.

When Tutunui arrived in shallow water he shook his body, but Kae ignored him and urged him forward. Soon Tutunui shook his body again, then suddenly he became stuck. Kae then dismounted, and as Tutunui struggled to free himself Kae killed him. He and his people then cooked Tutunui and ate him.

When Tinirau smelled the cooking fires he realised what had happened to his pet. He assembled a troop of dancers and taught them a magical dance that would lull their audience to sleep. He then told them that they would recognise Kae by his crooked teeth.

The troop left for Kae's village, where they performed songs and dances. When Kae opened his mouth and laughed they saw his crooked teeth and recognised him. The dancers then lulled everybody to sleep with the dance, and carried Kae to Tinirau, who killed him to avenge Tutunui's death.